Ancient Chinese Jades

from the Buffalo Museum of Science

by Joan M. Hartman

April 3 through June 15, 1975

GALLERY HOURS
MONDAY THROUGH FRIDAY 10-5
SATURDAY 11-5
SUNDAY 2-5

*The Gallery will be closed
all Holidays*

CHINA HOUSE GALLERY • CHINA INSTITUTE IN AMERICA
125 EAST 65TH STREET, NEW YORK, NEW YORK 10021

COURSES AT CHINA INSTITUTE

The School of General Studies of China Institute offers courses in Chinese Art, History, Culture, Philosophy, Music, Literature, Calligraphy, Painting, Cookery and other subjects.

China Institute is dependent upon its Associates for their annual support and on friends, corporations and foundations for contributions. Gifts to China Institute are deductible for federal income tax purposes. New friends are urged to make themselves Associates in one of the following categories: Student Associate $15.00; Regular Associate $25.00; Contributing Associate $50.00; Supporting Associate $100.00; Gallery Sponsor $500.00; Patron $1,000.00 or more.

China Institute is a non-profit and non-partisan educational institution, chartered by the Board of Regents of the University of the State of New York.

CATALOGS PUBLISHED BY CHINA HOUSE GALLERY

COVER: Animal Placque
H. 2 1/16"
Late Western Chou (Middle Chou)
Catalog No. 79

Preface

The Ancient Chinese Jades exhibition is the eighteenth in a series of loan exhibitions presented at China House Gallery. We are greatly indebted to the Board of Managers of the Buffalo Society of Natural Sciences for lending one hundred and twenty-six objects of jade from the collection of the late Chauncey J. Hamlin to China House Gallery, and especially grateful to Dr. Virginia L. Cummings, Director of the Buffalo Museum of Science, for her invaluable assistance in the preparation of the exhibition. These jades, donated to the Society by Chauncey Hamlin, have been housed in the Buffalo Museum of Science; we are privileged to be the first to exhibit a major portion of this collection publicly. We are also privileged indeed to have had a dedicated scholar, Joan M. Hartman, select the jades to be displayed and write the exhibition catalog. Her willingness to assume the responsibility of guest curator upon very short notice is deeply appreciated.

We wish to express our sincere thanks to all the volunteers for their loyal service to the Gallery, and to Mrs. Guy A. Weill for her talks to school and adult groups who return year after year to hear her speak. We are pleased and grateful that this exhibition is supported by a grant from the National Endowment for the Arts in Washington, D.C., a Federal agency.

F. Richard Hsu, *President*
China Institute in America

Acknowledgments

THANK YOU . . . to Dr. Virginia L. Cummings and Mr. Clifford Awald of the Buffalo Museum of Science, for their advice, cooperation and infinite patience . . . to Mrs. Edward M. Pflueger and Mr. John M. Crawford, Jr. for their friendship and confidence in me . . . to Mrs. Betty Schenck and Miss Amy McEwen for their scrupulous supervision of the catalog publication . . . to Michele Cole for countless small favors . . . to Mr. LeMar Terry and Mr. Cleo Nichols for once again creating a harmonious setting in which to display these jades. To all the scholars, past and present, who have set down their thoughts in writing so that others may find clues to the mystery which pervades Chinese art, particularly Chinese jade . . . I am deeply grateful.

Joan M. Hartman

Chronology

Neolithic — ? — 1700 B.C.

Shang Dynasty — ? 1700-1028 B.C.

Chou Dynasty — 1027-256 B.C.
    Western Chou — 1027-771 B.C.
    Eastern Chou — 770-256 B.C.
        Warring States — 480-221 B.C.

Ch'in Dynasty — 221-206 B.C.

Han Dynasty — 206 B.C.-220 A.D.
    Western Han — 206 B.C.-9 A.D.
    Eastern Han — 25-220 A.D.

Introduction

Chauncey J. Hamlin was a man of infinite energy and determination, coupled with an intellectual capacity which led to early financial success. Public spirited in the American tradition, he was largely responsible for the construction of the building known as the Buffalo Museum of Science, and served as President of the Buffalo Society of Natural Sciences, parent association of the museum, for twenty-eight years. Mr. Hamlin traveled to foreign climes extensively, each time bringing home artifacts which form a sizable nucleus of the museum's holdings. In the 1930's he visited China twice, for a stay of eighteen months each trip, and avidly studied the people, customs, language and culture of the Chinese. His hand-written journal abounds with enthusiastic as well as astute commentary regarding festivals, burial customs, food, costume and general impressions of the warmth of the Chinese. Once again, he acquired treasure for "his" museum— ceramics, bronzes and a fine collection of ancient jades. He was also zealous about building an excellent library of books on Chinese art at the museum. It is not sufficient simply to admire Chinese art. We must learn to understand why and how these articles were made, thus acquiring a deeper appreciation of these exquisite carvings.

Included in this catalog and the accompanying exhibition are 126 of the over 300 examples in the collection, selected for their quality, rarity, subject matter and/or unusual function. Fortunately, the group spans the late Neolithic period (circa 2000 B.C.) through the Han Dynasty (206 B.C.-220 A.D.), enabling us to see the development of early Chinese culture.

Most of these pieces are tomb articles, gleaned from grave sites in many different areas of China, their exact provenance unknown. Recent archaeology has shed light upon the styles of particular periods, and assisted us in the dating of some of these examples. However, the evidence is still too widespread to pinpoint a specific type as indicative of a particular area in this vast country. Where the author has come across comparable material published in archaeological journals, it is so stated under the description of the appropriate example. Lacking definite archaeological comparison, specimens are often likened to those in public and private collections.

While tomb furnishings evoke morose sentiments in the West, we should remember that death to the Chinese did not bear the same unhappy import. Surely they wept at the loss of a loved one, but the soul or spirit of the deceased would go on to the next world (paradise or heaven) if proper preparations were taken. Thus, there was the belief in rebirth, the extension of life after death, the fervent hope that he or she who had died would negotiate with the gods of the universe on behalf of those who remained on earth. An elaborate system of rituals evolved with respect to ancestor worship. It was important to keep one's ancestors content so they would perform in the desired manner. The tomb was abundantly supplied with food, wine, precious objects—all the plenty that the revered relative had enjoyed while alive. Invariably, and for good reason, jade is present in the Chinese tomb.

Jade was the hardest stone available to the neolithic Chinese and it offered attractive color tones. Farming implements were fashioned to serve many tasks. The *pi* (No. 2 et al.) represented heaven and religious practices took root at this early time. By the Shang Dynasty (circa 1600 to 1028 B.C.) when metal tools became common, beautifully fashioned blades were cut for use in ceremonial rituals and as symbols of rank for the official class. Sometime between late Shang and early Chou (circa 1028 B.C.) this extremely durable mineral assumed the function of preserving the precious soul of the deceased for its resurrection in the next world. Small amulets and, occasionally, carvings in the round were created to be sewn to the clothing of the corpse, suspended from the girdle, worn as jewelry and to stop the orifices of the body.[1] The dead was surrounded with symbols of heaven (*pi*), earth (*ts'ung*) and other appropriate objects. Royal tombs from Han times have yielded corpses completely clothed in jade shrouds, each composed of over two thousand placques linked with gold or silver thread.[2] Chêng, Tê-k'un quotes Confucian philosophy from the *Shuo wên chieh tzu,* a dictionary written in the second century A.D., which reflects Chou principles: "It (jade) has five virtues: there is warmth in its lustre and brilliancy, this is the manner of kindness; its soft interior may be viewed from outside revealing (the goodness) within, this is the manner of rectitude; its note is tranquil and high and carries far and wide, this is the way of wisdom; it may be broken but cannot be twisted, this is the manner of bravery; its sharp edges are not intended for violence, this is the way of purity."[3]

Jade continues to be of major importance in Chinese culture through the ages, but we are here concerned only with these early periods.

There is no evidence that jade, often referred to as nephrite[4] was ever found within the original eighteen provinces of China. Watson mentions the Lake Baikal area of Siberia as a source of nephrite in Neolithic and Shang times,[5] and there are numerous literary references to the importation of rough boulders from Eastern Turkestan (present day Sinkiang province), traditionally an independent empire. For instance, Willetts states, "In his report in chapter 123 of the first great Chinese history, *Shih chi* (P. 174), the explorer Chang Ch'ien notes much jade-stone in Khotan, which he visited about 125 B.C. He adds that Khotanese jade was collected and transported to the Emperor, and implies that the trade was of long standing."[6] The mountains near Khotan and Yarkand yielded rough boulders of green, brown, white and black in varying tones and combinations; the river beds and streams carried pebbles which suited smaller carvings. We do not know the extent of Chinese contact or trade with foreign places in ancient times. It is possible, of course, that there were sources of jade material, now long depleted, on home soil.

Nephrite is extremely hard, measuring 6.5 on Moh's scale which serves as the mineralogists' measure for same (the diamond hits the top at 10). Its specific gravity is 2.90-3.01, and because of its complex, fibrous structure the stone offers much resistance to the lapidary's tools. West states that mineralogically nephrite falls into the tremolite-actinolite family, its fibrous composition "tightly felted or matted together and the compact, tufted structure which results accounts for its extreme toughness."[7] Jade cannot be easily whittled like wood or ivory. It takes a combination of metal tools and abrasive paste composed of dampened, crushed minerals (quartz, garnets, corundum) to slowly abrade the stone into the desired shape and design. Prehistoric implements, fashioned before the advent of metal tools, were cut with laminae of sandstone or slates, and shaped with sandstone rubbers. Perforations were done with wood, bone or bamboo drills used in a rotary manner in conjunction with the abrasive paste.[8] By Shang times, metal tools were available, though not always used. Chêng, Tê-k'un mentions the invention of the rotary disc to cut boulders to the desired size[9] and further states, "The wheel, the tube and the point . . . were all operated by a rotary apparatus." The same author indicates that to produce straight holes (rather than conical or bi-conical perforations created by wood or bone drills) "the Shang jade-smith used a drill-point harder than corundum in his work, a tool almost as hard as a diamond drill."[10] Leather buffing wheels used with mineral paste produced the polished surfaces. The above information has been deduced from close study of the workmanship of these jades, as the framework for the treadle lathe and other machinery was made of wood and none has survived. Indications are that the methods employed in ancient days continued in much the same manner into modern times.[11] Jade factories today use electricity to turn the various drills, rather than the foot treadle method, but the basic techniques remain the same as in early periods.

Shang jades are specific in shape, the blades sharply cut, sometimes beveled (see No. 22). These are thought to have been used for ceremonial practices by this time, as metal weapons and agricultural implements, now available, were more durable. Placques of this period often have geometric designs in double line relief (see No. 16). Middle Chou (late Western Chou—circa tenth to eighth centuries B.C.) examples sometimes show a "shadow" groove next to the raised line motif (see cover and Nos. 77-80). Chêng describes "the effect . . . (as) bold and lively showing a new departure from the traditional technique. . . ."[12] The ingenuity and skill of the late Chou (circa 770-256 B.C.) carver is unlimited (see Nos. 83 and 84). Small amulets and toggles were designed for wear on the person before and after death. Aiding the lapidary in the execution of these superlative designs was the advent of iron tools, circa 400 B.C.[13] Thus, we see a progression of techniques and skills culminating in late Chou and continuing through later periods.

The dating of jades is extremely difficult. We study the kinds of perforations. If the hole is conical (comes to a point on one side) or bi-conical (cut from two sides), the method is considered neolithic and indicative of pre-historic date, as the softer bone or bamboo drill head wore away in the boring process. However, neolithic technique continued into Shang times and later, the new, harder drill points (which produced perfectly round, evenly edged perforations) slowly infiltrating the workshops. We then resort to cover-all terminology—"Neolithic method" or "Neolithic or Shang." By the same token, straight perforations indicate Chou cutting, but whether early, middle or late we cannot be sure since primitive methods persisted in later periods as well. Style, shape, decorative motif and subject may help to establish dates. The Chou conquerors employed Shang jade carvers in the early years, so that distinguishing between late Shang and early Western Chou jades is sometimes impossible. Hence, the label "Shang or Western Chou." Salmony stated, "There is no artistic break between the end of late Eastern Chou and the Han period so that attributions to either are sometimes a matter of conjecture."[14] Again, we must rely on analysis of subject and of style.

Science offers no help in dating jades. The stone itself, being a natural substance, is milleniums old in contrast to ceramic which is man-made, fired and subject to thermoluminescence testing. We are interested in the date of the cutting or fashioning of these jades, not determinable in the laboratory. Incrustations of earth, mineral deposits, painted or sprinkled pigments are equally undatable. Art historians depend upon stylistic analysis, interpretation of subject matter, symbolism, cutting methods as indicated above, and that which the archaeologist's spade has uncovered in controlled excavations.

Lest the reader be totally disillusioned with the value of twentieth century science, we hasten to relate certain definite findings in the laboratory, as well as ideas which should provoke further investigation. It is common knowledge that the ancient Chinese carved many varieties of stone.

Generally speaking, art historians have noted this in passing, but usually labeled archaic examples as nephrite, although Salmony sometimes described particular examples as "stone" rather than jade.[15] Examination of approximately twenty-five "jades" in the Buffalo collection under the x-ray diffraction machine and spectrographic scanning[16] reveals patterns which indicate that the overwhelming majority of these pieces (selected for their questionable appearance to the naked eye) fall into the tremolite-actinolite category (nephrite). As nephrite is usually more difficult to cut due to its structure and resultant hardness than soapstone, serpentine and other stones of similar color, it is significant to note that the Chinese preferred jade, probably because of its fascinating color properties, and the challenge it presented to the cutter's skills. They respected the toughness of the material, likening it to the finest character in man, as witness the writings of Confucius quoted earlier. Archaic jades often have buff, ivory to chalky-white areas, a result of burial underground. The term "calcified" applied to this characteristic indicates that the original nephrite or other stone has changed composition, has actually turned to calcite or calcined material. This theory has proved inaccurate. Julia Handy of the University of Pennsylvania finds that "X-ray diffraction analysis of a number of altered artifacts reveals that the white areas are not calcite. They have the same crystal structure as the unaltered areas. . . ." West corroborates this by stating, "It has been noted that this surface alteration, as determined by x-ray diffraction, is not a different mineral but merely a softened form of nephrite."[17] Even when the example is completely altered and appears opaque (we will adopt the term "altered" as a more accurate definition of the change of color) it is possible to determine, through x-ray diffraction and scanning electron microscopy, whether the specimen is nephrite or another mineral (see No. 7). No matter how experienced the eye, it is not possible to ascertain positively whether an example is nephrite or something similar, without laboratory examination. Jades which appear altered are often "softer" so that the knife test for hardness is invalid (and, of course, there are some stones which are as hard as jade, so this method is quite unreliable). Even when the example doesn't show discoloration to the naked eye, the material may have softened due to burial.[18] In the present catalog, objects are identified as nephrite or other stones. There is no question, however, that the majority of carvings executed in early times are nephrite.

Over the years it has been assumed that the composition of the soil in which the jade was buried, the moisture and oxygen in the atmosphere of the tomb, all contributed to the alteration of jades as well as other artifacts. Handy and Gaines postulate that the alteration "consists of a selective dissolution (leaching) along grain boundaries by high-pH ammoniacal solutions produced during decay of the corpses with which the jades were buried." They continue, "There appears to be no correlation between the degree of alteration of nephrite artifacts and their archaeological age or their length of burial. Thus, chemical 'weathering' due to the action of soil moisture does not seem to be a viable explanation for the observed alteration . . . the alteration takes place in relatively short times (months?), and that it is produced by the action of high-pH (basic) rather than acidic solutions."[19] West partially agrees with this hypothesis in writing, "Evidently water leaches chemicals from the soil and the resulting solutions attack the surface of the jade. Decomposition products of bodies in the tombs would undoubtedly accelerate this attack."[20] The present writer does not necessarily endorse this thesis. However, it is interesting to consider the possibility that alteration of these archaic jades was caused by the rapid deterioration of the corpse in the tomb and its close proximity to the jades. Concerning alteration of material, Clifford Awald of the Buffalo Museum notes that the rind on raw nephrite boulders, created by nature's own weathering process, was sometimes incorporated into the carving by the lapidary. In burial, this pre-altered section of the carving would be inclined to break down more rapidly.

While the art oriented individual may not find these scientific studies particularly stimulating, it is pertinent to understand the reasons for the alteration of these jades, and important to recognize that the identification of the stone itself is readily at hand through laboratory analysis, but not easily determined on casual examination. Invariably, those examples which appear to be a stone other than nephrite prove to be genuine jade when subjected to testing. As nephrite offers special challenges to the lapidary's skills, and was highly esteemed in traditional China, it is considered more valuable than other minerals.

Another characteristic of these ancient jades remains to be discussed. In addition to the incrustation of earth which adheres to the surface of many of these jades, traces of red pigment are often found. This pigment is usually referred to as "cinnabar."[21] Occasionally, it is identified as "vermilion"[22] and from time to time simply "red pigment."[23] Tests done on a number of these jades at the University of Pennsylvania indicate the red pigment to be hematite (iron oxide). Gettens identifies "the bright red pigment that was used in earliest times in painted ornamentation and in red stamp ink, and also for strewing over the dead in burial . . . as the mineral cinnabar . . . a simple compound, the sulphide of mercury."[24] He adds, "Cinnabar deposits are found in Asia, in the Altai, and in the Ferghana region of Russian Turkestan which have been worked for quicksilver for a thousand years. In China it occurs in the provinces of Kweichow and Hunan. . . ."[25] Gettens also says, "At some time during Han . . . a way was found to make cinnabar artificially by combining the elements mercury and sulphur and then by subliming the red product in clay retorts. This dry-process, artificial product, which we now call vermilion, was purer, brighter, and more highly valued, than powdered cinnabar. Its preparation in China continues to the present day."[26] He says, "Iron oxide also was used at all periods. . . ." and mentions its "ocherous color."[27] It would seem that the Chinese used the red materials readily at their disposal at a given site, or selected their favorite from the group described above. There is ample evidence from the tomb for the practice of using red pigment. Chêng describes burials at Pan-po (Neolithic culture-circa 3600 to 4200 B.C.) as showing "the disposal of the dead inside a settlement, and the use of red pigment in connection with burial recalls the Palaeolithic funerary customs practiced by Upper Cave Man at Chou-k'ou-tien."[28] The custom apparently stretches back before Neolithic times. Treistman mentions that the Chinese circa 1000 B.C. "treated their dead with red ochre" and the people of Eastern Siberia, circa 5000 to 2000 B.C., sprinkled red ochre in the death ritual.[29] Chang, Kwang-chih speaks of red ochres used in Neolithic burial customs.[30] That the practice of using pigment in burials, on the deceased and on the furnishings of the tomb continued into later periods is verified by Tsien who indicates that incised inscriptions on Shang oracle bones are sometimes "filled with vermilion for illumination"; he goes on to mention inscriptions on Shang tortoise shells of cinnabar.[31] He also refers to Shang jades excavated at An-yang by the Academia Sinica with inscriptions written in "vermilion characters."[32] Waley affirms this by discussing late Chou burials as revealing red pigment on human remains and objects interred.[33] Hansford, in discussing late Chou pottery, writes, "The practice of strewing red pigment on *ming ch'i* (burial goods) in ancient China was wide-spread. . . ."[34] Salmony refers to Pelliot when stating that vermilion or ochre was "placed in the grave at the time of burial."[35] And the recently exhumed body of a 2100 year old woman from Ma-wang-tui, Ch'ang-sha, Hunan Province, dated Western Han (206-24 A.D.) was immersed in a red liquid in the innermost coffin. Chemical analysis "showed it was acidic, containing several organic acids and a compound of mercury. Slightly antiseptic and disinfectant, the liquid helped prevent decay."[36] This last would seem to be the key to the symbolism of the pigment. Johnson states that in ancient China "Cinnabar and gold were considered as medicines *par excellence,* and were frequently used in combination with excellent results in the attainment of immortality. . . . Cinnabar was also a favorite ingredient in life-prolonging concoctions, by virtue of its producing mercury, the 'living metal', when subjected to heat."[37] Waley profers similar ideas when stating that ". . . it is certain that cinnabar was one of the most important 'life-giving' substances sought for by the ancient Chinese."[38] De Groot states that the writing of the burial tablet at the time of interment was done in red ink "because red is the colour of fire and light and consequently particularly indentified by Chinese philosophy with the Yang or the chief principle of life."[39] Johnson speaks of these drugs used by Taoist Immortals and quotes from *Pao Pu Tzu: Nei P'ien,* Chapter II, "superior grade of medicine causes the human body to be at peace, protracts its life, enables it to ascend and become a celestial spirit, to saunter about above and below, causing all spirits to serve it."[40] Thus, we see that the deceased, along with his favorite possessions and special tomb furnishings was to be preserved with the red pigment which guaranteed immortality, the ascension of the soul or spirit to heaven, the universe, the supernatural. The use of "spirit cinnabar" or "magic cinnabar" (and we can include hematite in this context) as Waley terms it[41] appears to have survived into later times. Gascoigne mentions the great Sung Dynasty scholar-writer, Su Tung-p'o (eleventh century A.D.) seeking the desirable elixir of life and noting in his journal "how Po Chü-i (772-846 A.D.), famous poet of the T'ang Dynasty, had set about it long ago on more conventional lines, constructing a special furnace at his country cottage. Po had tried to fuse sulphur and mercury in accordance with a recipe of the second century A.D. He failed—perhaps fortunately, since the idea was to eat the mixture. . . ." but he wrote a poem relating his effort, the last two lines of which read, "A pinch of the elixer would have meant eternal life; A hair-breadth wrong, and all my labours lost!"[42] Whether in life or after death the magic red powder would guarantee immortality! These archaic jades, then, imbued with their own preservative powers, when sprinkled with red powder or painted red doubly emphasized the wish for survival, renewal of the life spirit, the essence of man, beyond earth and the tomb.

It has been said that archaic jades are "dry" material, repetitious, miniscule in size, too esoteric to provide much aesthetic satisfaction. Yet careful study reveals a wide variety of ornamentation, superlative craftsmanship, intriguing folk lore and spiritual mysticism. Jade, most precious of stones to the Chinese, embodies a vast treasury of symbolism, faith and artistic genius, so much a part of the very being of this ancient people.

Notes

1. Chêng, Tê-k'un, Archaeology in China, Vol. III, *Chou China,* 1963, P. 188. Dr. Chêng discusses jade found at Chung-chou-lu, late Western Chou and states that these examples prove "dressing the corpse with jade had its beginning in Western Chou."

2. See *Archaeological Treasures Excavated in The People's Republic of China,* Tokyo National Museum, 1973, No. 95; *The Genius of China,* Royal Academy, London, 1973, No. 139.

3. Chêng, Tê-k'un, Archaeology in China, Vol. II, *Shang China,* 1960, P. 109.

4. We are not here concerned with jadeite, a stone imported by the Chinese, probably not earlier than the 18th century from Burma (see Hansford, S. H., *Chinese Jade Carving,* 1950, P. 22).

5. Watson, Wm., *Cultural Frontiers in Ancient East Asia,* 1971, Pp. 59, 60.

6. Willetts, Wm., *Chinese Art,* Vol. I, 1958 (Penguin paperback), P. 60.

7. West, E. H., "Jade: its Character and Occurrence," *Expedition,* Vol. 5, No. 2, 1963, P. 3 (top right).

8. Hansford, S. H., *Jade-Essence of Hills and Streams,* 1969, P. 17.

9. See Footnote No. 3, P. 119.

10. See Footnote No. 3, P. 120.

11. For photographs of jade apparatus in the 1930's see Hansford, S. H., *Chinese Jade Carving,* 1950, Plates III-XI, and by the same author, see Footnote No. 8, Pp. 18, 19.

12. See Footnote No. 1, P. 187.

13. See Footnote No. 8, P. 20; Watson mentions, "Archaeological evidence . . . points to the earliest casting (of iron) . . . about 400 B.C." Watson, Wm., *Early Civilization in China,* 1972, P. 82.

14. Salmony, A., *Carved Jade of Ancient China,* 1938, P. 68.

15. For example: Salmony, A., *Archaic Chinese Jades from the Collection of Edward and Louise B. Sonnenschein,* 1952, P. 18, Nos. 3, 4.

16. X-ray diffraction and spectrographic analysis (scanning electron microscopy) work done at the University of Pennsylvania by Julia L. Handy and Alan M. Gaines. Additional examination of a similar nature was undertaken by Joseph Mazza and Norman Kenny of NL Industries, Inc., TAM Division.

17. See Footnote No. 7, P. 5 (top right).

18. See Gure, D., "Notes on the Identification of Jade," *Oriental Art,* Vol. III, No. 3, 1951, P. 115.

19. Gaines, A. M. and Handy, J. L., "Alteration of Chinese Tomb Jades: A Mineralogical Study," Dept. of Geology, University Of Pennsylvania, Philadelphia, Pa.,—paper presented at National Geological Society of America, Miami, Nov., 1974.

20. See Footnote No. 7, P. 5 (top right).

21. See *An Exhibition of Chinese Archaic Jades,* C. T. Loo, Inc., Norton Gallery of Art, 1950, Plate XXXVI, No. 2 et al.; Footnote No. 8, P. 58, Nos. A86, A87 et al.; d'Argencé, R., *Avery Brundage Collection Chinese Jades,* 1972, P. 48, Plate XVII, No. B60J453 et al.; Loehr, M., *Ancient Chinese Jades,* 1975, P. 71, No. 62 et al.

22. See Footnote No. 15, P. 62, No. 1 et al.

23. See Dohrenwend, D., *Chinese Jades in The Royal Ontario Museum,* 1971, P. 42, No. 930.21.277 et al.

24. Gettens, R. J., "True and False Vermilion on Early Chinese Ceramics (1)," *Far Eastern Ceramic Bulletin,* Vol. VI, No. 1, March, 1954, P. 18.

25. Gettens, R. J. and Feller, R. L. and Chase, W. T., "Vermilion and Cinnabar," *Studies in Conversation,* 17, (1972), P. 46.

26. See Footnote No. 24, P. 18.

27. See Footnote No. 24, P. 20.

28. Chêng, Tê-k'un, Archaeology in China, Vol. I, *Prehistoric China,* 1966, P. 81.

29. Treistman, J. M., *The Pre-history of China,* 1972, P. 61 and 30 respectively.

30. Chang, Kwang-chih, *The Archaeology of Ancient China,* revised edition, 1968, P. 375.

31. Tsien, T. H., *Written on Bamboo and Silk,* 1962, P. 26 and 28 respectively.

32. Ibid., Pp. 83, 84.

33. Waley, A., "Notes on Chinese Alchemy," *Bulletin of The School of Oriental Studies,* London Institution, 1930, P. 18. The writer is grateful to Barry B. Blakeley, Seton Hall University, for the suggestion that the clues to the symbolism of this red pigment can be found in references to ancient Chinese alchemy.

34. Hansford, S. H., "Hui Hsien Pottery in the Collection of Mr. Dennis M. Cohen," Oriental Ceramic Society Transactions, 1951-53, P. 76.

35. See Footnote No. 14, P. 5.

36. "Study of a Body 2,000 Years Old," *China Reconstructs,* October, 1973, P. 34.

37. Johnson, O. S., *A Study of Chinese Alchemy,* 1928, P. 59.

38. See Footnote No. 33, P. 19.

39. de Groot, J. J. M., *The Religious System of China,* Vol. I, Part I, 1892, P. 216.

40. See Footnote No. 37, P. 58.

41. See Footnote No. 33, P. 19.

42. Gascoigne, B., *The Dynasties and Treasures of China,* 1973, Pp. 136, 137.

43. Evidence of the use of red pigment by cultures other than the Chinese is abundant. Gettens states that "Cinnabar is found as a paint pigment in remains of nearly all the early civilizations" (see No. 24, Ibid, P. 18). And Ritchie, in describing the high incidence of red ochre in Indian Burials of New York State says, "There is also, one feels sure, a good deal of lost symbolism, some of it of more universal nature, in which high places, the East, the sun, fire and red ochre figure as elements of a vigorous religious movement, apparently founded upon the perpetuation of life after death. . . ." Ritchie, Wm. A., *The Archaeology of New York State,* 1969, rev. ed., P. 178.

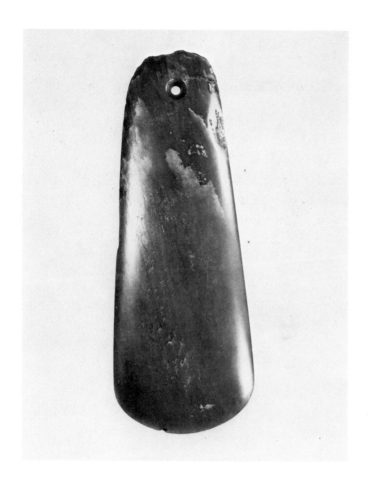

Numbers in bold type refer to bibliography entries. See page 80

1.
Axe
Dark green variegated nephrite
L. 8″
Neolithic or Shang

Heavy blade with fine cutting at bottom edge, bi-conical perforation. Soft polish on all surfaces. Parts of edges appear unfinished. Chipped. There seems to have been a strong northern tradition for this kind of blade in early times. Andersson wrote, "This group of axes occupies a broad belt on the Sino-Mongolian borderland from North Shensi in the west to Joho in the east" (**No. 1**, P. 48). A blade of similar type, without perforation, is published by Okladnikov, A. P. (*Materials and Researches for The Archaeology of U.S.S.R.,* No. 43, Moscow-Leningrad, 1955, P. 198, Fig. 88 (left)).

Exhibited: **No. 9**, Exhibition No. 26.

Comparable examples: **No. 4**, P. 41 (top); **No. 9B**, P. 32, No. 1; **No. 12**, Plate 25 (left); **No. 6**, 1973, No. 5, P. 267, No. 12.

2.
Pi (Symbol of Heaven)
Brown and buff altered stone
Diam. 15½″
Neolithic or Shang

Unusually large disc with slightly conical center perforation. Wheel marks on one side. Chipped. Twenty character archaic style incised inscription of later date. There are a number of these Shang jades with similar inscriptions, but they have not been proven authentic (see **No. 9B**, P. 15 for discussion of same).

3.
Pi (Symbol of Heaven)
Mottled buff and brown stone
Diam. 5″
Neolithic or Shang

Heavy disc with soft, allover polish.
Conical center perforation. Straight-edged,
uneven shape.

4.
Axe
Brown and black altered stone
L. 6¾″
Neolithic or Shang

Heavy blade with bi-conical perforation,
allover polish. Chipped.

Comparable example: *Ch'uan Kuo Chi Pen
Chien-shieh Kung-cheng Chung Tsu Tu
Wen Wu Chang Lang T'u Lu (Illustrations
of Chinese Cultural Objects Excavated
at Construction Sites (all over China) since
1949)*, Vol. 2, Peking, 1955, P. 123,
No. 1 (left); also **No. 6**, 1974, No. 2,
P. 113, No. 2.

5.
Fish
Grey altered stone, incrustation of soil
L. 14¾"
Neolithic or Shang

Heavy slab with incised fish on both
sides. Conical hole and another incomplete
which shows neolithic technique. Damaged
and repaired. Salmony cites fish of this general
type as having prototypes in Siberia of the
Neolithic age (see **No. 10**, Plate II, Nos. 1,
2). The present example was probably
suspended and used as a chime. Chêng states
that these stones were used in sets of three
(in Shang times)—see **No. 3A**, P. 225.

Waterbury mentions that fish symbolized
ample harvest to the ancient Chinese (Waterbury, F., *Early Chinese Symbols and Literature:
Vestiges and Speculations,* 1942, P. 106).
Primitive as the representation of the fish
(probably carp) is, there is an upsweep to the
bifid tail, slight arch to the body, and a wide-
eyed naiveté.

Comparable example: **No. 3A,**
No. 2; Gyllensvard, B. and Pope, J., *Chinese
Art from the Collection of H. M. King
Gustaf VI Adolf of Sweden,* The Asia
Society, Inc., 1966, P. 53, No. 61.
For a later example recently excavated, but
in the same tradition, see **No. 5A**, Plate 4.

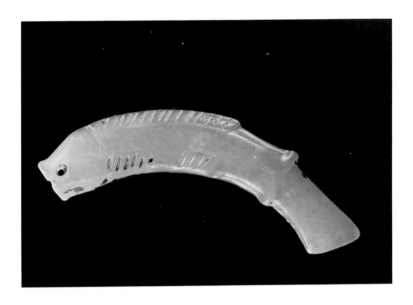

6.
Fish
Pale green nephrite
L. 2½″
Shang

Pendant, carved in the round. Incised details (similar on reverse), conical perforation. Soft allover polish.

Comparable examples: **No. 7**, 1955, No. 9, P. 17, second photo section, No. 13; **No. 3A**, P. 117, Fig. 24, No. 18.

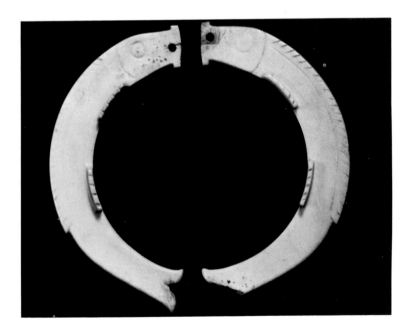

7.
Pair of Fish
Ivory color nephrite, completely altered
L. 3″
Shang

Arched backs, incised features, flange fins (similar on reverse), bifid tail (one broken). Great animation and vitality. We expect the two to straighten out and swim off at any moment. X-ray diffraction analysis has shown this pair to be nephrite, though they are completely altered to an even ivory, opaque appearance.

Comparable example: **No. 6**, 1965, No. 5, P. 10 (front photo section), No. 5 (second from top right).

8.
Animal Placque
Pale green and brown altered nephrite, incrustation of soil
L. 3″
Shang

Low relief representation of mythological animal with arched back and closed paw (same decoration on reverse). Soft allover polish. Two conical holes, probably used to attach placque to clothing. There is strength and ferocity to the image.

Comparable example: **No. 13,** 1972, No. 8, P. 24, No. 1.

9.
Handle
White altered nephrite, incrustation of soil
L. 3½″
Shang

Simple block style with two relief bands toward top. Bottom round butt to fit into bronze socket at top of dagger handle. Soft allover polish.

Comparable examples: **No. 13,** 1972, No. 7, P. 7 (bottom), No. 1; **No. 13,** 1972, No. 8, P. 24, No. 2.

10.
Handle
Green and buff altered nephrite
L. 4½"
Shang

Relief decoration of "leaf-like" motif, a
double line toward the top. Conical hole near
bottom. Some polish remains. Similar on
reverse. May have been broken and cut sharp
at base. Handle for bronze blade (see
No. 9B, P. 109, No. 117 for similar handle
used in this manner).

Comparable examples: **No. 9B, P.** 109,
Nos. 112, 113, 114.

11.
Arrowhead
Pale grey and buff altered nephrite
L. 2¼"
Shang

Sharp-pointed, beveled, with soft allover
polish (the same on reverse).

Comparable example: **No. 3A,**
Plate XIV, C.

12.
Disc with Double Flange
Completely altered ivory color nephrite, incrustation of soil, red pigment
Diam. 3½"
Shang

Disc has incised circular lines on both sides. Flanges damaged. Outer circumference uneven. Soft allover polish. Watson states that these rings are descended from Lungshan (Neolithic, circa 2nd millenium B.C.) prototypes which originated in Siberia. The Shang people added the flanges and wore them as bracelets (**No. 12A**, P. 39, 59). Its function as a bracelet is corroborated by Hansford who cites a burial at Gua Cha, Kelantan, Malaya in which the skeleton was found wearing the ring on its arm (**No. 5A**, P. 72, Plate 9).

Exhibited: **No. 9**, **No. 12**.
Comparable example: **No. 5B**, P. 36, **No. A16**.

13.
Disc with Double Flange
Olive green and buff altered nephrite
Diam. 3½"
Shang

Stone is translucent with a soft allover polish. Probably worn as bracelet (see preceding example).

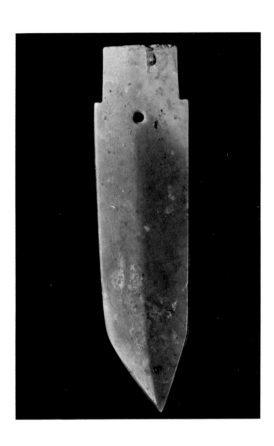

14.
Dagger
Grey-green and buff altered nephrite
L. 2¾"
Shang

Miniature blade beveled from center (same
on reverse). Conical perforation. Classified by
Chêng as a *Kuei* sceptre (**No. 3A**, P. 117,
Fig. 24, No. 7) and probably hung from the
girdle as symbol of rank.

Comparable example: **No. 7**, 1955, No. 9,
P. 19, second photo section.

15.
Bow Tip
Pale green and black nephrite, red pigment
H. 5¼"
Shang

Heavy pendant with low relief representation
of human face in profile, stylized pointed
ear (same on reverse). Soft allover polish.
Slightly conical perforation through ear.
Chêng illustrates a bow tip like this as typi-
cally Shang (**No. 3A**, P. 117, Fig. 24, No.
17). In describing Shang military equipment
Salmony speaks of "gem stones on the bow
... (consisting) of a perforated full round
human or animal head, flattened on four sides
and appearing above a comparatively large
curved tusk. These two parts are joined by a
narrow section which is concave in front...
the excavator found pairs... bound together
and inserted into the bow tips. In each
instance, the concavities of the pair held the
bowstring." (**No. 10C**, P. 43 (bottom)).

Published: **No. 11**, Plate 59, No. 46.

Comparable example: **No. 7**, 1955, No.
9, P. 19, second photo section, No. 2.

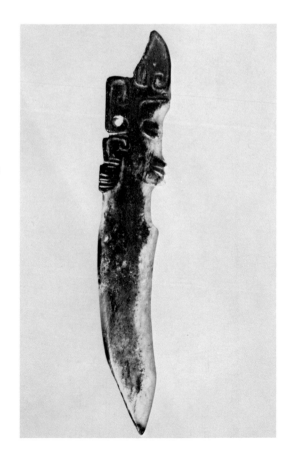

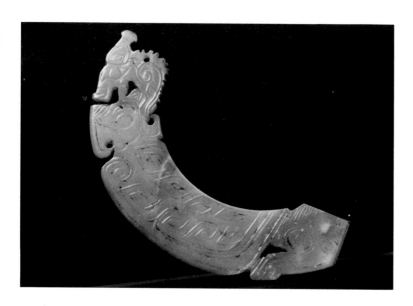

16.
Cockatoo with Dragon Crest
Pale green altered nephrite
H. 3¾"
Shang

In profile, the motif executed in double-line low relief (similar on reverse), three slightly conical perforations at top. The bird is surmounted by a crest in the form of a *kuei* (dragon found on Shang bronze vessels) with single horn. Incised lines indicate tail feathers and upturned leg.

  Published: **No. 10A**, P. 17, Fig. 2;
  No. 10C, Plate XI, No. 5.

17.
Placque with Human Face
Pale green and buff altered nephrite
H. 3⁷⁄₁₆"
Shang or Western Chou

Human figure in profile with high crown. Countenance, body with bent arm, clenched fist, raised leg, cut in double line low relief. Imitative of Shang bronze decoration. Lower rump has incised circle with crossed lines. Treatment similar on reverse. Allover soft polish. The projection at bottom worn. These anthropomorphic representations have not been satisfactorily interpreted, but there is an urgency and intensity about the image that must be indicative of a fascinating tale.

  Published: **No. 10C**, Plate XII, No. 2;
  No. 10A, Fig. 5.

  Exhibited: **No. 9**, No. 91.

  Comparable examples: **No. 5A**, Plate 18B;
  No. 4, P. 53.

18.

Buffalo
Mottled buff altered nephrite
L. 2½″
Shang

Placque with features in low relief. Conical perforation through head. Reverse is flat, with a few incised lines. Some traces of polish remain. Damaged. The animal rests comfortably, his great hulk benign, his expression friendly, at peace with the world.

Comparable examples: **No. 9B**, P. 125, No. 152; **No. 10B**, Plate XX, Nos. 6, 7.

Reverse

19.

Cockatoo
White and pale yellow altered nephrite
H. 2¹⁰⁄₁₆″
Shang

Flat plaque depicting bird with high crest in profile. Meticulously carved with incised and relief detail (similar on reverse). The wing structure is composed of fanciful curls, the crown trimmed in multiple lines with ridged outer edge. Soft allover polish.

Comparable examples: **No. 10**, Plate XVII, No. 5; Hartman, J. M., *Chinese Jade Through The Centuries,* China Institute in America, 1968, P. 15, No. 7.

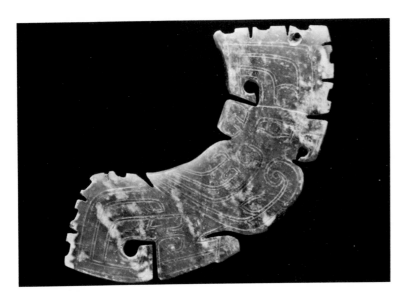

20.
Cockatoo
Pale green and buff altered nephrite
H. 4¾"
Shang or Western Chou

Flat placque of bird in profile, with high crest, hooked beak and full tail feathers, worked in double line low relief (similar on reverse). Conical perforation through crown. Allover soft polish. The cutting is crude in comparison to Nos. 16 and 19, and may indicate an early Western Chou date rather than Shang.

Published: **No. 9**, No. 83.

Comparable example: **No. 10**, Plate XVII, No. 2.

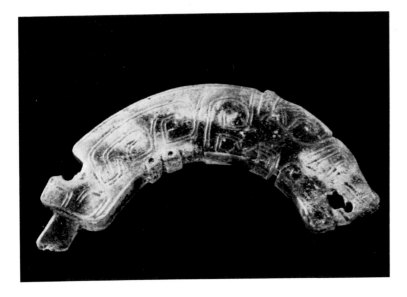

21.
Monster
Green and buff altered nephrite, incrustation of soil
L. 3"
Shang or Western Chou

Placque with double line relief (same on reverse), representing a dragon or mythological beast with ferocious face. Perforation through teeth. Soft allover polish. Damaged. Butt end for indeterminable function.

22.
Dagger
Buff and brown altered nephrite
L. 4"
Shang or Western Chou

Blade tapers from center, beveled and incised, above a *t'ao-t'ieh* mask in double line low relief (similar on reverse). Conical hole near top. Tang probably held bronze handle. Soft allover polish. Some chips.

For an example of comparable shape and beveling: **No. 13**, 1972, No. 8, P. 30, No. 2. For an example with similar *t'ao-t'ieh:* **No. 9B**, P. 73, No. 67.

23.
Miniature Dagger
Green and buff altered nephrite, red pigment
L. 2¾"
Shang or Western Chou

Double beveled blade on either side from center. Incised lozenge and line pattern on band under incised tang. Conical perforation. (Similar on reverse). Damaged. Probably suspended from girdle as symbol of rank.

Comparable examples: **No. 10B**, Plate X, No. 3; **No. 9B**, P. 61-63.

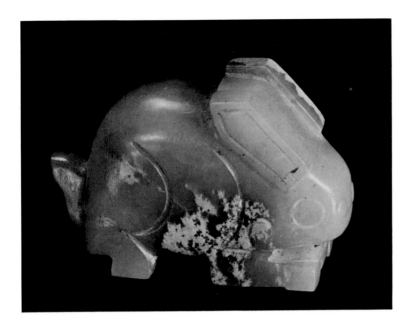

24.
Rabbit
Pale green and buff altered nephrite
L. 1¾"
Shang or Western Chou

Figures in the round are comparatively rare
at this early date, the present example most
unusual. The animal crouches, his features
incised. A conical perforation runs through
front paws. In Chinese mythology, the hare
resides on the moon, pounding the drugs
which produce the elixir of immortality. This
animal is also the fourth of the Twelve
Terrestrial Branches (12 Zodiac Animals).
Whether this symbolism goes back as far
as the present example is not known. However, the rabbit on the moon is illustrated on
a painted banner recently exhumed from a
Western Han tomb at Ma-wang-tui (**No.** 13,
1974, No. 7, center photo section, upper
left corner of banner), and there are Eastern
Chou and Han literary references to the
use of the zodiac animals (Hartman, J. M.,
"An Interesting Han Jade in The Los Angeles
County Museum of Art," *Artibus Asiae,*
Vol. XXXVI½, 1974, Pp. 61, 62). As
1975 is the year of the Hare, we are assured
of prosperity and plenty.

25.
Bird
Grey altered nephrite incrusted with soil
H. 1¾"
Shang or Western Chou

Similarly decorated on both sides with
incised and relief details. Broken proboscis.

Comparable example: **No.** 7, 1955, No. 9,
P. 17 (second photo section), No. 6.

26.
Cicada
Black nephrite
H. 1¾″
Shang or Western Chou

Figure in the round with outspread wings, the head with beak, all features quite worn. The reverse represents back of insect with two conical perforations drilled horizontally for suspenion. Chipped. The cicada develops underground for 13 to 17 years, before burrowing its way to the surface, attaching itself to a stalk, breaking out of its nymphal skin and emerging an adult of its species. The ancient Chinese, ever observant of nature's creatures, likened this remarkable process to the resurrection of the soul after death. Thus, we find representations of the cicada on Shang bronzes and other artifacts. There are several stylistic variations in jade as seen herein. This example appears to relate to a bird in the Royal Ontario Museum (**No. 4, P.** 43) the technique and general style quite similar, the features equally worn, although the reverse is flat. Another example of this variety is in the collection of Chêng, Tê-k'un, Cambridge, England.

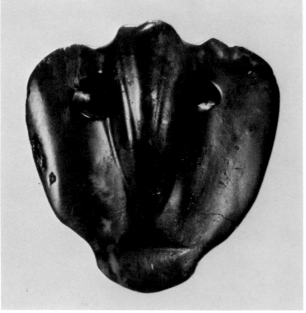

Reverse

27.

Cormorant

Grey and buff altered nephrite

H. 2¼"

Shang or Western Chou

Depicted in repose, eyes, wing structure and other details cut in relief and incised (similar on reverse). Corner of tail repaired. The cormorant was trained by the Chinese to fish, it being expert at this task (Ball, J. D., *Things Chinese,* 2nd Ed., 1893, Pp. 109-111). A strap was placed about its neck to prevent the greedy bird from swallowing its catch, but part of the haul was shared at the end of the day's work. Perhaps its placement in the tomb indicated ample food or plenty for the dead.

Comparable example: Chêng, Tê-k'un, "The Carving of Jade in The Shang Dynasty," Oriental Ceramic Society Transactions, Vol. 29, 1954-55, Pp. 13-30, Plate 6, Fig. 19.

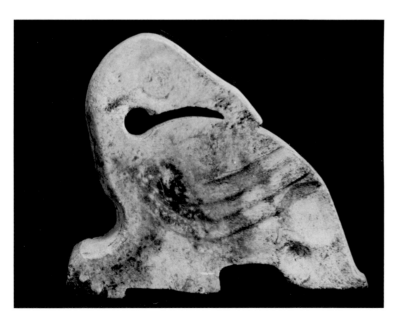

28.

Cormorant

White altered nephrite

H. 1¼"

Shang or Western Chou

Bird in reclining position with head back, relief carving (similar on reverse). One side has chips at end of tail. Some polish remains. See preceding example for explanation of the function of this bird.

29.
Bird
Grey and buff altered nephrite, incrustation
of soil
L. 1¾"
Shang or Western Chou

Flat placque with incised features (similar
on reverse), a conical perforation through
chest. The blunt-nosed, plump creature,
swathed in feathers, sits comfortably, its facial
expression alert but not unfriendly.

Comparable examples: **No. 3A**, P. 117,
No. 16; **No. 5B**, P. 55.

30.
Bird
Buff and white altered nephrite, incrustation
of soil
L. 2"
Shang or Western Chou

Almost identical with No. 29.

31.

Frog
Pale green altered nephrite
H. 2"
Shang or Western Chou

Crouching frog with eyes in low relief, open mouth and incised paws. Conical perforation through center. Uncarved and flat on reverse. Some traces of polish remain. The creature is ready to take advantage of the next opportunity.

Exhibited: **No. 9, No. 75.**

Comparable examples: **No. 3A,** Plate XVII; b; *Chinese Art from The Collection of James W. and Marilynn Alsdorf,* The Arts Club of Chicago, 1970, No. J5.

32.
Bird
Green, grey and white altered stone,
red pigment
L. 2″
Shang or Western Chou

Similar incised decoration on both sides;
perforation through chest. Broken and
repaired. This delightfully sturdy creature
waddles along at a brisk pace.

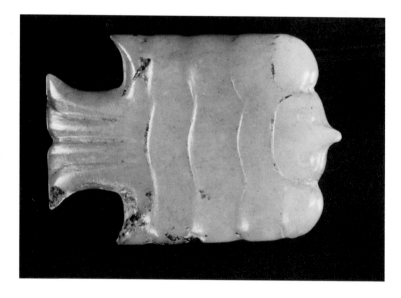

33.
Bird
Grey-white altered nephrite, incrustation
of soil
L. 1½″
Shang or Western Chou

Low relief cutting, with soft allover polish.
Reverse has incised lines on wings and perforation. In repose but aware of potential
danger. Probably used as a toggle hung from
the girdle. While the face is of a familiar
type (**No. 4**, P. 60), the body conformation
is unusual, its rounded contours and "mellow"
polish offering tactile satisfaction.

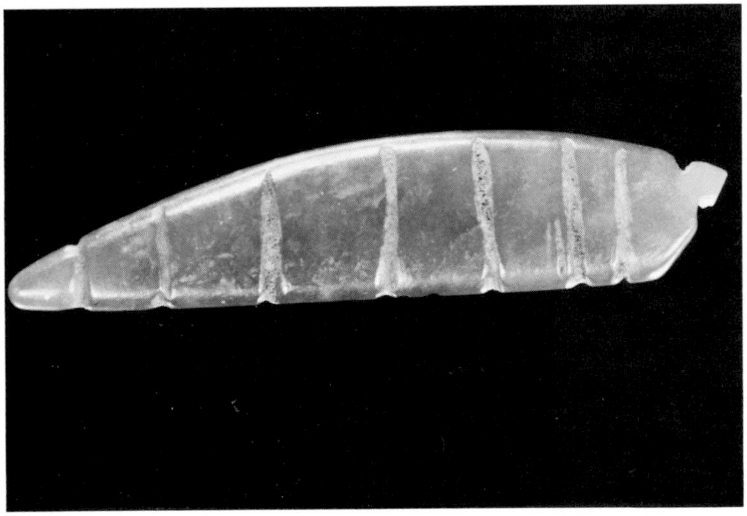

34.
Chrysalis
Green nephrite, incrustation of soil
L. 1 5/16″
Shang or Western Chou

Pendant with incised lines around body, projection at one end, perforation through same. Soft allover polish. This example and the following (Nos. 34–38) are usually classified as silkworms. However, it is virtually impossible to identify the species in its undeveloped (pupa) stage. Once again, however, the connotation of new life must have had significance for the Chinese. The deceased was to be reborn in heaven.

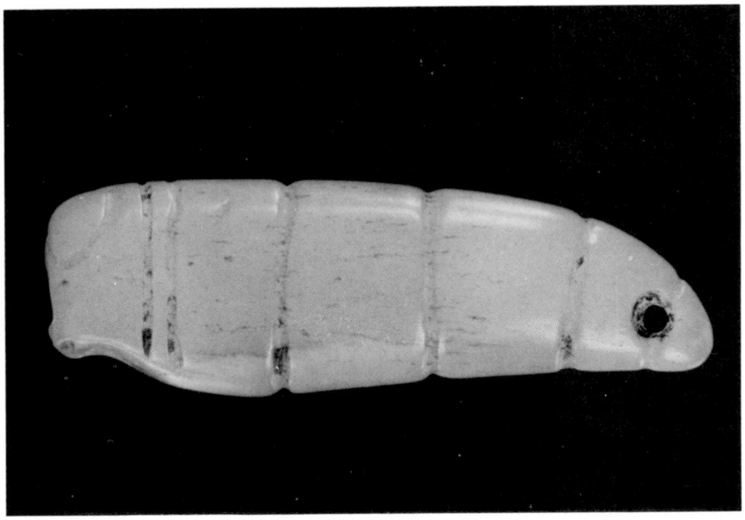

35.
Chrysalis
White nephrite, incrustation of soil
L. 1 1/8″
Shang or Western Chou

Incised lines encircle body, a conical hole at either end. Soft allover polish. Bulbous "eyes" at one end. For a discussion of these jade pupae as representative of various stages in the development of insects see No. 10B, P. 74, Paragraph 3.

Comparable example: No. 5A, Plate 19 (lower right).

36.
Chrysalis
Pale green and white altered nephrite,
incrustation of soil
L. 1″
Shang or Western Chou

Incised banding around body, conical perforation through tail.

37.
Chrysalis
Green and white altered nephrite incrusted
with soil
L. 1″
Shang or Western Chou

Incised banding around body, perforation.
The features are worn. There is much realism
in these miniature carvings.

Comparable example: No. 9B, P. 212,
No. 310.

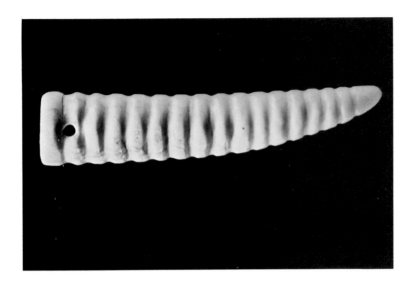

38.
Chrysalis
White altered nephrite
L. 2¼"
Shang or Western Chou

Incised banding around body, soft allover polish, perforation through tail.

Comparable examples similar to the entire group included herein: **No. 10B**, Plate XLI, Nos. 9-15.

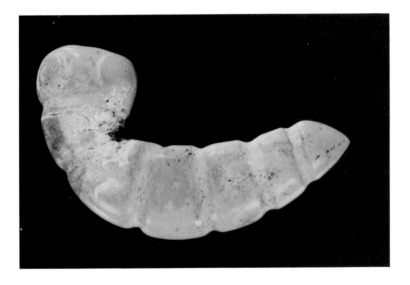

39.
Chrysalis
Pale green and white altered nephrite
L. 1⅛"
Shang or Western Chou

Incised banding around body, rather flat on reverse, perforation through one end. Bulbous "eyes" at broad end. Soft allover polish. Probably a Hammerhead beetle, which slithers sinuously along the ground.

40.

Fish

Pale green and buff altered nephrite, incrustation of soil

L. 2¼″

Shang or Western Chou

Incised and relief details, conical perforation with rim relief serving as eye of the fish. Beveled where incised fins appear. Bifid tail. Chêng represents this type as Western Chou (**No. 3B**, P. 187, No. 6), although a comparable example from a Shang tomb is published in **No. 7**, 1951, No. 5, Part I, P. 10, photo section, No. 8.

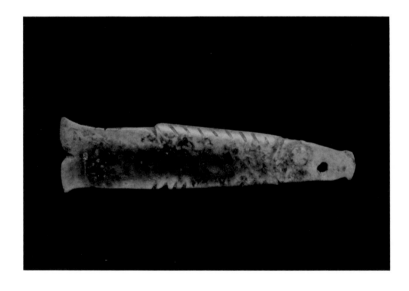

41.

Fish

Pale green and buff nephrite, incrustation of soil, red pigment

L. 2⁵⁄₁₆″

Shang or Western Chou

Similar to the preceding, but in addition to conical perforation the eye is represented in low relief on one side, similar treatment around perforation (rim relief) on reverse.

42.

Animal Mask
Pale green nephrite
H. 1⅛"
Shang or Western Chou

Features are incised. Soft allover polish. The reverse is concave and undecorated. A conical perforation runs from back to front edge at bottom. Decoration in the tradition of early bronze. The face is regal, imbued with power.

43.

Animal Mask
Grey altered nephrite, incrustation of soil
H. 1½"
Shang or Western Chou

Carved in double line relief, the top of horns and central tuft on forehead incised. Back is concave, the perforation conical. Soft allover polish. There is a strength to the image — stringent eyes, exaggerated nostrils, powerful horns—a creature to be reckoned with despite its small size.

44.

Animal Mask
Buff altered nephrite, red pigment
H. 1½"
Shang or Western Chou

Incised decoration, soft allover polish. Plain back. Two slightly conical perforations. A study of these few examples reveals marked differences in features and workmanship.

> Comparable example: *Chinese Archaic Jades,* C. T. Loo, Inc., Norton Gallery of Art, 1950, Plate XXI, No. 6.

45.

Animal Mask
Pale green altered nephrite, incrustation of soil
H. 1"
Shang or Western Chou

Same type as the preceding. Relief carving, soft allover polish, the back undecorated, three conical perforations running from back to front. While an attempt has been made to achieve the impact of the other examples, the close-set eyes and snub nose offer an amusing rather than a formidable presence. Masks of this type have been identified by Chêng (**No. 3B**, P. 187, Fig. 16, No. 4).

46.
Bead
Yellow altered nephrite
L. 1½″
Shang or Western Chou

Incised line motif with notched sides. The
reverse undecorated, to lie flat. Perforation
runs vertically through length of piece. High
polish. Probably part of a necklace.

47.
Ring
Grey-white altered nephrite, incrustation of
soil
H. 1¼″
Shang or Western Chou

Ribbed banding on exterior. Smoothly
polished inside and out. An example of the
finest workmanship.

   Comparable example: **No. 9B**, P. 136,
No. 172.

48.

Pi (Symbol of Heaven)
Green, brown, black and yellow nephrite
Diam. 4″
Shang or Western Chou

Allover soft polish with tool mark on one side. Conical perforation. Precision cut, straight outer edge.

Comparable example: **No. 5B**, P. 32, No. A1.

49.

Pi (Symbol of Heaven)
Pale green, brown and buff altered nephrite
Diam. 7⁵⁄₁₆″
Shang or Western Chou

Softly polished circle with conical central orifice. "Rolled" outer edge running thin at one end. Broken and repaired. Symbols of heaven and earth (*ts'ung*) are found interred with the dead from Shang times on, and the *pi* earlier (Watson, Wm., *Early Civilization in China*, 1972, P. 31, Plate 13; **No. 3**, Plate 15).

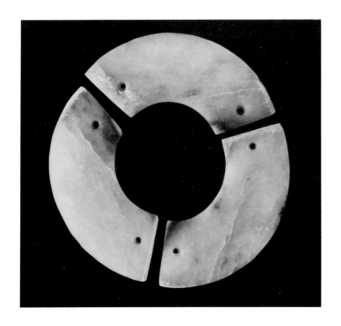

50.

Three-sectioned Disc
Grey and brown altered nephrite
Diams. 3¾", 4", 4"
Shang or Western Chou

Three arcs cut with straight edges. Two conical perforations at end of each placque. Soft
allover polish. Cut from the same boulder.
Repaired.

Comparable example: **No. 13**, 1972, No. 4,
P. 33, No. 4.

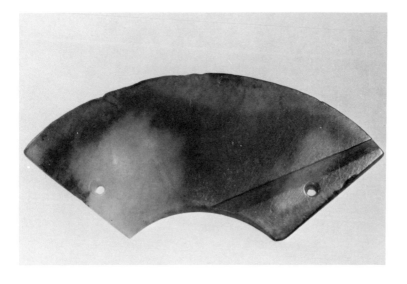

51.

Section of Disc
Grey, dark brown and rust nephrite
L. 4"
Shang or Western Chou

Conical hole at each end. Soft allover polish.
Tool mark on one side. From a set of placques
like the preceding.

Comparable examples: **No. 5B**, P. 35,
No. A12; **No. 9B**, P. 393.

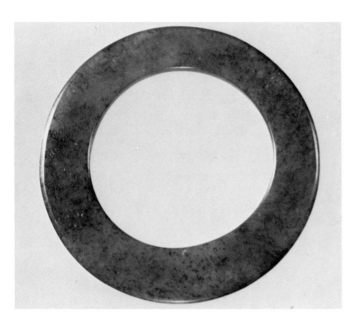

52.
Disc
Pale green and rust-brown nephrite
Diam. 3¾"
Shang or Western Chou

Skillfully executed with "rolled" outer edge
as well as center orifice. Width of circle
uneven. Soft allover polish. Probably
descended from Neolithic type which originated in the Lake Baikal region of Siberia
(**No. 12A**, Plate 17).

    Comparable examples: **No. 5B**, P. 34,
Nos. A, A9.

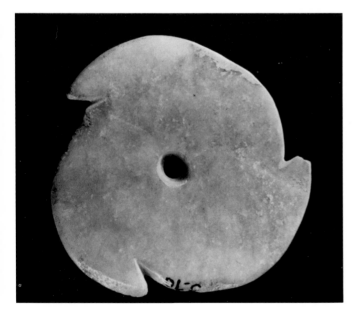

53.
Spindle Whorl
Grey-white and buff altered nephrite
Diam. 1¾"
Shang or Western Chou

Disc with three projecting points. Conical
perforation through center. Soft polish.
Uneven surfaces show imperfection of
workmanship.

    Comparable example: **No. 6**, 1973, No. 5,
P. 267.

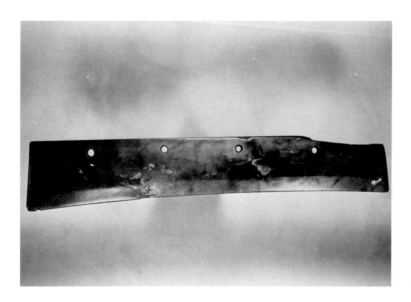

54.
Knife
Pale to dark green altered nephrite
L. 15½"
Shang or Western Chou

Beveled cutting edge (on reverse as well),
four conical perforations. Soft allover polish
except for one edge at narrow end. Salmony
suggests that thongs may have been passed
through the holes to bind the blade to a
wooden shaft (see reference below).
Chipped.

  Published: **No. 14**, Plate 3B; **No. 10A**,
  P. 18; **No. 11**, P. 56, No. 21.

  Comparable example: **No. 9B**, P. 165,
  No. 211.

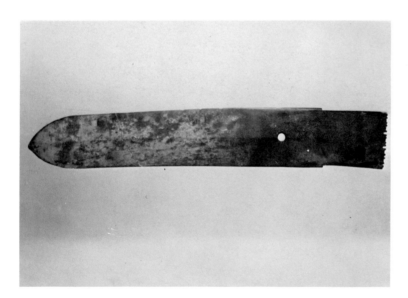

55.
Dagger
Mottled charcoal black stone incrusted with
soil
L. 17¼"
Shang or Western Chou

Long blade, beveled from center on both sides,
tapers to thin cutting edges. Tang notched,
probably to grip a bronze handle. Perforation
slightly conical. Soft allover polish. Broken
and repaired.

56.
Dagger
White and brown altered nephrite
L. 5¾"
Shang or Western Chou

Beveled from center and edges. Conical hole.
Soft polish on all surfaces. Chipped.

57.
Dagger
Moss green altered nephrite with black flecks,
incrustation of soil, red pigment.
L. 2¹⁰⁄₁₆"
Shang or Western Chou

Blade has double beveling on either side of
center (same on reverse). Conical perforation. Soft allover polish. These miniature
blades are thought to have been suspended
from the girdle as symbols of rank.

Comparable example: **No. 5B,** P. 49.

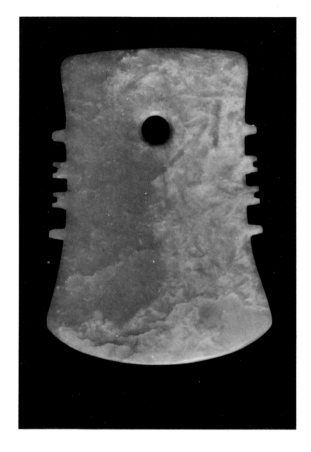

58.

Axe
Dark green variegated nephrite
H. 6½"
Shang or Western Chou

Heavy blade with "rolled" edges and soft
allover polish. Bi-conical perforation.
Chipped.

59.

Axe
Pale green, buff and rust nephrite
L. 4⁴⁄₁₆"
Shang or Western Chou

Well-shaped blade with notches at each side,
probably designed to hold rope which
fastened wooden handle. Conical perforation.
Some polish remains.

Comparable example: **No. 5B**, P. 62,
No. A100.

60.

Axe
Dark green and buff translucent nephrite
L. 4¾"
Western Chou

Thin cut stone of exquisite translucency.
Front of blade tapers to even thinner cutting
edge at bottom. Front full and softly polished.
Reverse quite flat, imperfectly polished, bears
tool mark. Perforation slightly conical, but
well rounded.

 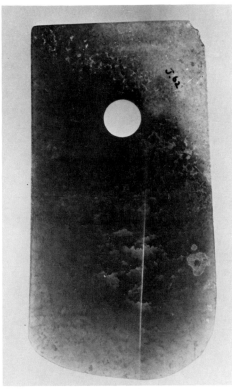

Reverse

61.

Axe

Green and brown mottled nephrite
L. 5⁵⁄₁₆″
Western Chou or later

Heavy blade with smoothly "rolled" edges, including perforation which is drilled from one side and smoothly polished. Blade has soft allover polish. Damaged.

Comparable example: **No. 14**, Plate 2A.

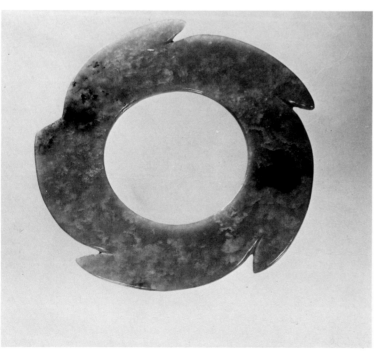

62.

Disc with Notches

Pale green, brown and black mottled nephrite
Diam. 5½″
Western Chou

Disc with "rolled" edges including perforation. Soft allover polish. Notches probably cut at a later date.

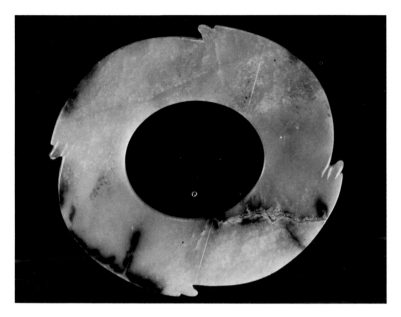

63.

Disc with Notches
Pale green and brown nephrite incrusted with soil
Diam. 5 11/16"
Western Chou

Probably re-cut at a later date. Center perforation conical. Tool marks on one side. Soft allover polish, including perforation.

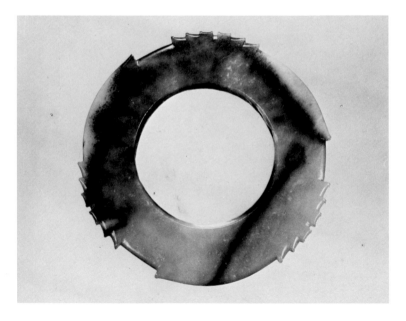

64.

Disc with Notches
Grey, yellow, dark brown and black nephrite
Diam. 5"
Western Chou or later

Ring with three sets of notches, having "rolled" outer edges including notched sections. Soft allover polish including perforation which is slightly conical.

Published: **No. 10A,** P. 16, Fig. 1.

Exhibited: **No. 9,** No. 14.

Comparable example: **No. 10B,** Plate XXXI, No. 1 (example is cruder than present example, but of similar type).

65.

Ts'ung (Symbol of Earth)
Beige mottled stone
H. 12 1/16"
Western Chou

Heavy cylinder with square exterior. Hole
bored through from either end, ridge at
center interior where drills did not meet. Soft
exterior polish.

Comparable example: **No. 9A, P. 51,**
No. 46.

66.

Head of Buffalo
Green nephrite, incrustation of soil
H. 1½"
Western Chou

Details incised, ears "scooped" for realism.
Conical perforation. Soft allover polish.
Reverse undecorated and flat. Chipped. The
workmanship is crude and characteristic
of Western Chou, when the jade carver seems
to have struggled to retain skills as well
as create new styles.

Comparable example: **No. 9B, P. 126,**
No. 154.

67.

Head of Buffalo
Grey and buff altered nephrite, red pigment
H. 1 7/16"
Western Chou

Incised and relief details. Conical perforation.
Soft allover polish. Reverse flat and undecorated. Chipped. Sowerby identifies this
animal as Bubalus mephistopheles, "an
extinct species of Buffalo" represented in
Shang art and "subsequently copied by the
artists of the Chou period." He distinguishes
these "wide flat sharply sloping horns"
from those of the ordinary ox and the water
buffalo (Sowerby, A., *Nature in Chinese Art*,
1940, P. 76). The ox is emblematic of
spring (renewed life) and is the second of
the Twelve Terrestrial Branches (Zodiac
Animals). See catalogue No. 24 for references
to the use of the Zodiac system in ancient
times.

Reverse

68.
Pair of Birds
Pale green and brown nephrite, brownish-green stone, incrusted with soil
H. 1″
Western Chou

Incised eyes, pointed noses, the bodies having three horizontal lines in relief, bifid tails. The reverse is flat and undecorated. Soft allover polish.

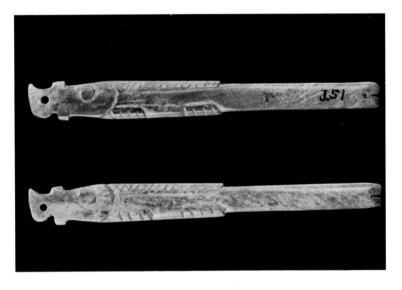

69.
Pair of Fish
Olive green altered nephrite, incrustation of soil, red pigment
L. 3⅛″
Western Chou

Incised and relief details (similar on reverse, but flat), conical perforations, bifid tails. Soft allover polish.

Comparable example: **No. 10B, Plate XLV, No. 1.**

70.
Bird
Pale green and brown nephrite
L. 1¾"
Western Chou

A less elaborate version of Nos. 29 and 30.
Incised details and eye in relief (reverse
similarly decorated). Conical perforation
through chest. Soft allover polish.

Comparable example: **No. 9B, P. 195.**

71.
Animal
Green pinite, red pigment
L. 1 9/16"
Western Chou

Animal with arched back, bifid tail, the eye
in low relief (both sides similar). Conical
perforation. Soft allover polish. Broken and
repaired. There is an innocence about this
tiny creature, and an industriousness which is
quite remarkable when we consider its
minute size and rather crude workmanship.

72.
Rabbit
Green and black nephrite, incrustation of soil
L. 1⅝"
Western Chou

Incised details, the eye in relief (similar on reverse). Conical perforation. The animal crouches as if ready to spring. For symbolism of the hare see catalogue No. 24.

Comparable example: **No. 13,** 1972, No. 7, P. 7 (bottom), No. 3.

73.
Animal
Pale green and brown altered nephrite
L. 2"
Western Chou

Details incised (similar on reverse), allover soft polish, conical perforation through mouth. Crouching monster with upraised pointed tail. A cruder version of the Shang prototype (see **No. 9B,** P. 123, No. 147).

74.

Placque
Grey-white, brown and amber-yellow
translucent nephrite
Diam. 1 7/16"
Western Chou

Reticulated circular placque with incised
details of stylized animal. Reverse undecorated. Soft polish on both sides.

75.

Placque
Grey-white nephrite with black flecks
Diam. 1 9/16"
Western Chou

Almost identical with the preceding.

76.

Mask
Olive green altered pinite, incrustation of soil
H. 1″
Western Chou

Face (animal?) in relief with conical
perforation through forehead. Some polish
on raised surfaces. Reverse is undecorated.
The large round eyes have an eerie, ominous
expression.

77.

Animal Placque
Grey-green nephrite, incrustation of soil,
red pigment
L. 2¾″
Late Western Chou (Middle Chou)

Creeping monster with upturned, swirled tail,
the low relief details with characteristic
shadow groove. Decoration similar on both
sides. Two conical perforations. Soft allover
polish.

Exhibited: **No. 9, No. 81.**

Comparable example: **No. 10B,** Plate
XXXVII, Nos. 12, 13.

78.
Placque
Pale green and pale brown altered nephrite
H. 2″
Late Western Chou (Middle Chou)

Figure of bird incised with characteristic
shadow groove (decoration the same on reverse). Conical perforation at bottom. Soft
allover polish. The attitude is decidedly self-
confident!

Comparable example: **No. 9B**, P. 221,
No. 331; Gyllensvard, B. and Pope, J.,
*Chinese Art from The Collection of H.M.
King Gustaf VI Adolf of Sweden,* The Asia
Society, Inc., 1966, P. 57, No. 68.

79.
Animal Placque
Pale green altered nephrite
H. 2¹⁄₁₆″
Late Western Chou (Middle Chou)

Figure of an animal in profile with incised
details, having shadow groove effect (similar
on reverse). Soft allover polish. The well
delineated ear, curled nose, brisk beard, and
upturned paw complement a body covered
with curled and swirl motifs; a thoroughly
amusing, appealing composition.

80.
Handle
Buff altered nephrite
H. 4″
Late Western Chou (Middle Chou)

Double line relief cut and incised details, shadow groove, soft allover polish (similar on reverse). Animal composite including birds has a rhythm, portent of later Eastern Chou design.

Exhibited and illustrated: **No. 9**, No. 133; **No. 11**, P. 72, No. 124.

Published: **No. 10A**, P. 43, Fig. 6.

81.
Headdress Ornament?
Green and brown mottled nephrite, incrustation of soil
H. 4½″ (back wall)
Western Chou or later

Cylinder with high back wall, "rolled" smooth edges, tool mark on interior, soft allover polish. Chipped. Various uses have been proposed for this object. It is thought to have been used to scoop and measure grain; as a ceremonial sleeve cuff; as a headdress ornament. The lack of decoration and simple workmanship render it difficult to date this example.

Exhibited and illustrated: **No. 11**, P. 67, No. 83.

Comparable examples: **No. 2**, P. 50; **No. 5B**, P. 103; **No. 9B**, Pp. 216, 217.

82.
Belt Ring?
Pale green and buff altered nephrite
H. 1½"
Eastern Chou

Incised curl motif and diagonal lines. Soft allover polish. Decoration similar on reverse. Straight cut perforation which may have been done later, as it breaks into incised design on one side. An example of the deftness of the lapidary, so apparent during Eastern Chou.

83.
Long Bead
Grey-green pinite, red pigment
L. 2½"
Late Eastern Chou

Incised and relief design with allover soft polish (decoration the same on reverse). Read horizontally the design is that of tightly interlocked *kuei* (dragon) forms, each biting the other's tail, a ferocity which is, after all, quite tame. Perforation runs lengthwise through the center. Flaw in the stone across middle of one side. Chipped. Probably from a necklace.

Comparable example: **No. 9B**, P. 249, No. 372.

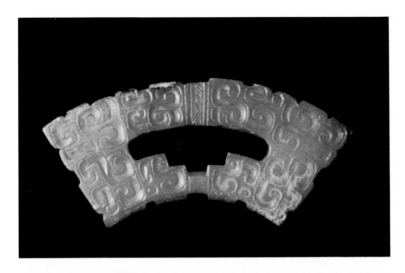

84.

Placque
Pale green and brown nephrite
L. 2$\frac{10}{16}$″
Late Eastern Chou

Incised and relief carving with soft allover polish. Decoration on one side depicts an animal in each corner biting a snake, situated back-to-back, and separated by fanciful decoration and central orifice. The reverse bears a curled repeat pattern, which is found on bronze vessels of the period. (Pope, J. A., Gettens, R. J., Cahill, J., Barnard, N., *The Freer Chinese Bronzes,* Vol. I, 1967, P. 496, Plate 91.)

Reverse

85.
Disc
White and buff altered nephrite
Diam. 1⁹⁄₁₆″
Late Eastern Chou

Relief and incised double curl motif (similar on reverse) with allover soft polish and "rolled" edges. Center perforation slightly conical. Probably from a set of girdle pendants.

Comparable examples: **No. 6,** 1964, No. 3, P. 7, front photo section, No. 12; *Loyang Chung-chou-lu,* Peking, 1959, P. 114, No. 2; **No. 4,** P. 40 (top).

86.
Disc
Green nephrite, incrustation of soil
Diam. 2¹⁴⁄₁₆″
Late Eastern Chou

Relief cut curl pattern (the same on reverse), with soft allover polish, "rolled" outer edge. Probably one of a set of girdle pendants.

Comparable examples: **No. 13,** 1974, No. 5, P. 75, Plate 29.

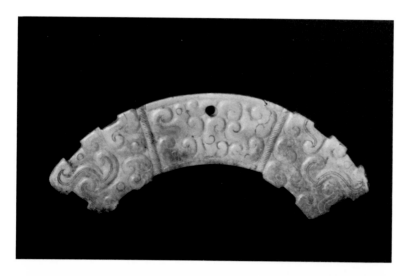

87.

Pendant

Variegated grey altered nephrite, incrustation of soil

L. 3″

Late Eastern Chou

Incised and relief cutting of repeat curls; a *kuei* (dragon) in profile at each end with diagonally incised collar (reverse has only one collar). Soft allover polish. Perforation for suspension at top. Probably part of a set of girdle pendants (**No. 3B,** P. 196, Fig. 18 (third row from top)).

Comparable example: **No. 6,** 1962, No. 12, P. 627.

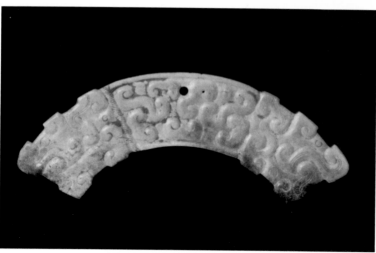

Reverse

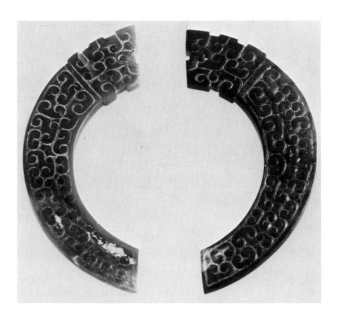

88.

Pair of Pendants
Dark green nephrite, incrustation of soil
L. 4"
Late Eastern Chou

Incised and relief pattern of repeat curls making up the bodies of the *kuei* (dragons). Design similar on reverse. A perforation at top of each pendant for suspension. Part of set of girdle ornaments used in pairs (see **No. 3B**, P. 196, Fig. 18, bottom).

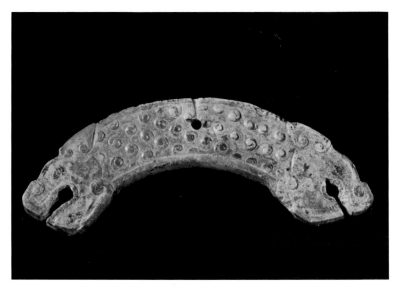

89.

Pendant
Pale green and buff altered nephrite
L. 2½"
Late Eastern Chou

Relief cutting of double dragons with curl motif (similar on reverse). Soft allover polish. Perforation for suspension as one of a set of girdle pendants.

Comparable example: **No. 4**, P. 40.

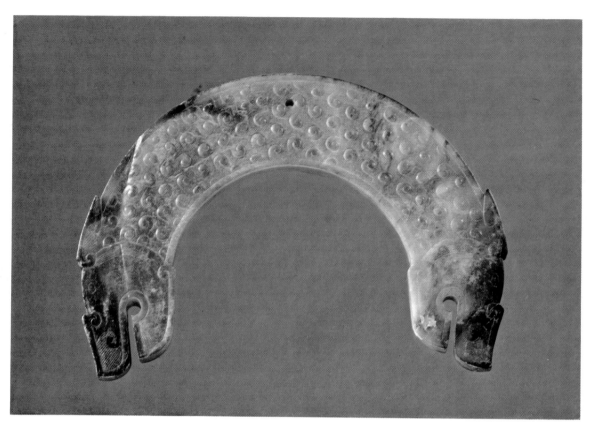

90.

Pendant

Pale green and brown altered nephrite
Diam. 4½"
Late Eastern Chou

Double dragon pendant with incised and
relief curl motif on body (similar on reverse).
Soft polish on all surfaces, but straight cut
edges bear a high polish. Perforation for suspension from girdle. Chipped and repaired.
Hansford writes that sets of girdle pendants
were a very popular part of court costume.
"These hung from the waist like a kind of
open-work apron, and tinkled as the wearer
walked. They were the pendants to which
Confucius referred as symbolical of propriety
and humility, and their sound as of the nature
of music." (**No. 5B,** P. 2ī)

91.
Pi (Symbol of Heaven)
Green nephrite, heavy incrustation of soil,
red pigment
Diam. 7¹¹⁄₁₆″
Late Eastern Chou

Incised relief curl pattern in central zone,
surrounded by narrow rim of diagonal incised
lines, the outer border incised with *t'ao-t'ieh*
masks connected by intertwining ribbons
(reverse similarly decorated). Straight cut
exterior edges including center perforation.
Microscopic scanning reveals that the red
pigment was painted on with a brush, and the
heavy soil coverage is superimposed on the
paint. Repaired. The *pi* was used in worship
as representative of Heaven from pre-historic
times (see catalogue Nos. 2, 3). Hansford
interprets the form as the "sun radiating
light in the vault of heaven, the sun being
conceived of . . . as the centre and source of
a creative force extending to the limits of the
universe." It symbolized "the Supreme Power
on high, the source of Man's life and the
arbiter of his destiny. . . ." (**No. 5,** P. 97).
Cammann postulates that the circular disc
represents the sky and the central orifice the
"Sky Gate", entrance to Heaven (Cammann,
S., "The Symbolism of The Cloud-Collar
Motif," *Art Bulletin,* XXXIII, 1, (1951),
1-9). Whatever your preference, and there are
other theories applied to this form, the *pi*
persisted as emblematic of Heaven into
modern times.

Comparable examples: **No. 9A,** P. 110,
No. 76; **No. 4,** P. 87.

92.

Pi (Symbol of Heaven)
Olive green and buff altered nephrite
Diam. 5″
Late Eastern Chou

Incised relief curl motif (similar on reverse),
with soft allover polish including straight
cut edges (outer and central perforation).
Chipped. In a study of these *pi* discs, Juliano
notes that late Chou spirals appear in a combination of clockwise and counter-clockwise
positions. However, examples dating to the
Han Dynasty show the curls in only one
direction, on a single example "either all
clockwise or all counterclockwise, but never
in both." (Juliano, A., "Late Chou Jades:
Significance and Dating of Raised Spiral
Ornamentation on Late Chou Pi Discs",
M.A. thesis, Oriental Studies, Graduate
School, University of Pennsylvania, 1968).
Recent archaeology has revealed a *pi* of
the present type and another like the
preceding (No. 91) which bear the incised
curls in both directions, from the Western
Han tomb of Prince Liu Sheng (Watson,
W., *The Genius of China,* 1973, P. 102,
Nos. 146, 148). It is possible that the style
persisted into early Han times and then
petered out, or that these examples may
actually emanate from the earlier Eastern
Chou period, placed in the tomb as favorite
antique heirlooms of the deceased. The
majority of jades in this form associated with
the Han Dynasty do seem to bear out Juliano's
theory.

Comparable example: *Ch'uan Kuo Chi
Pen Chien-shieh Kung-cheng Chung Tsu
Tu Wen Wu Chang Lang T'u Lu
(Illustrations of Chinese Cultural Objects
Excavated at Construction Sites (all over
China) since 1949),* Peking, 1955, Plate
119, No. 1.

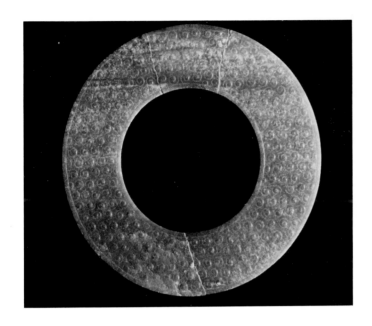

93.
Disc
Green, brown and buff altered nephrite
Diam. 6½"
Late Eastern Chou

Incised and relief curl motif (similar on reverse). Some polish remains. Broken. Hansford describes this decoration as "resembling grains of corn projecting above the surface of the soil . . . the curl doubtless represents the sprouting seed, and the whole is symbolical of fertility." (**No. 5**, P. 106)

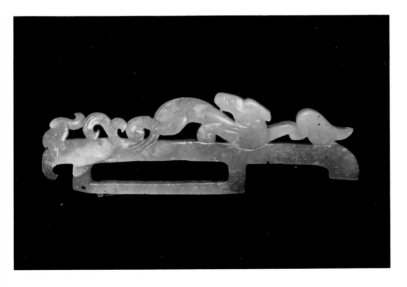

94.
Sword Scabbard
Grey-white and buff nephrite, incrustation of soil
L. 3⅛"
Late Eastern Chou

A sinuously curved animal surmounts the slide, its tail sweeping in full swirls, with extra furbelows at either end. Details are incised (same on reverse), and a soft polish covers all but the interior of the slide opening. There is a joie de vivre about this representation.

Exhibited and illustrated: **No. 9**, **No. 118**.

Comparable example: **No. 10**, Plate LVIII, No. 2.

95.
Button
Reddish-brown variegated nephrite
Diam. 1⅛″
Late Eastern Chou

Low relief curvilinear repeat pattern with diamond in center, on slightly convex surface. The reverse is irregularly flat with two conical horizontally drilled perforations. Soft allover polish. A double curl motif is incised on the back, as if the lapidary had intended to decorate this side like the front, but abandoned the plan.

Comparable example: *Chinese Archaic Jades,* C. T. Loo, Inc., Norton Gallery of Art, 1950, Plate LIX, No. 7.

96.
Scabbard Chape
Grey, brown and black nephrite
H. 1½″
Late Eastern Chou

Incised pattern (similar on reverse). Soft allover polish. Two small conical horizontal perforations at top. A third larger vertical perforation in center of top to take butt, attaching it to the base of the sword sheath.

Comparable example: **No. 7,** 1956, No. 4, P. 16, No. 8.

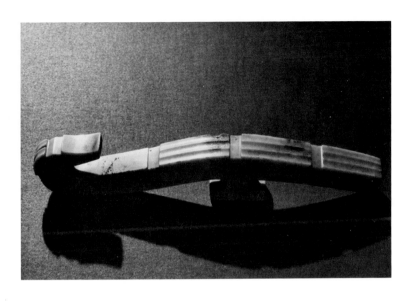

97.
Buckle
Buff and brown altered nephrite
L. 6 1/16"
Late Eastern Chou

Squared, simplified form of dragon buckle
with three zones of depressed tri-partite
columns, intersected by three depressed bands.
Straight cut sides. The top bears a high
polish. The polish is worn on other surfaces.
A rectangular knob on the back is fashioned
to hold one loop from a belt, while the
head of the buckle is ringed by the other.
The cross banding may have held metal inlay
originally, or jade inserts, the whole mounted
in gold or bronze (see No. 10C, Plate XVII,
No. 4).

Comparable examples: **No. 4**, P. 78;
No. 9B, P. 319.

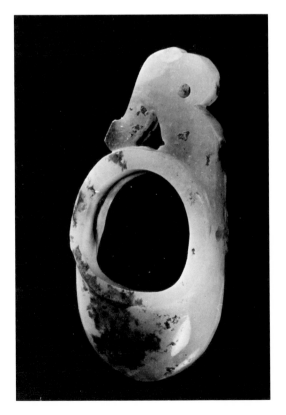

98.
Archer's Ring
Grey-white, yellow and rust nephrite
L. 1¾"
Late Eastern Chou or Western Han

Ring of oval shape. Bird in profile projects
on one side with incised eye (same on
reverse). Perforation on one side, probably
to anchor ring via chord to thumb. Soft
allover polish adds a mellow tactile quality.
Minor chips.

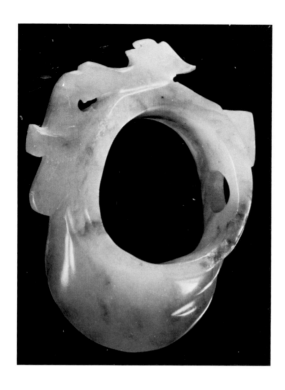

99.

Archer's Ring
Grey-white and brown altered nephrite,
incrustation of soil
L. 2⅛″
Late Eastern Chou or Western Han

Oval shape with figure of bird in profile at
top, a perforation through head, a perforation
at each side of ring. Soft allover polish.
These rings were designed to protect the
archer's thumb from the backlash of the
bow string.

Comparable example: **No. 10B**, Plate
CVII, No. 8.

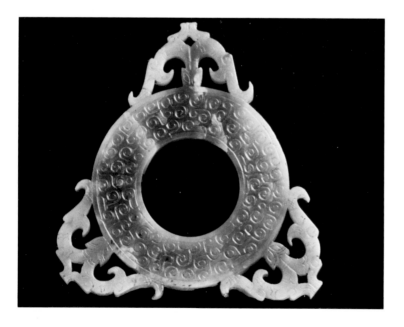

100.

Placque with Animals
Pale green altered nephrite, incrustation of
soil, red pigment
Diam. 3″
Late Eastern Chou or Western Han

Incised curvilinear pattern which has a steady,
rhythmic effect, the exterior edge having
three reticulated extensions in the form of
feline animals, details incised (decoration
similar on reverse). Soft allover polish.

Exhibited: **No. 9**, No. 15.
Exhibited and illustrated: **No. 11**, P. 74,
No. 154.

Published: **No. 10A**, P. 44, Fig. 7.

101.
Bangle
Pale green and brown altered nephrite
Diam. 4 9/16"
Late Eastern Chou or Western Han

Incised double curl interconnecting pattern
on both sides, with soft allover polish. Broken
and repaired. This design appears in various
versions on bronze vessels of the Late
Chou and Han dynasties, a close comparison a covered *ting* in the Ashmolean Museum,
Oxford (Watson, Wm., *Ancient Chinese
Bronzes*, 1962, Plate 66a).

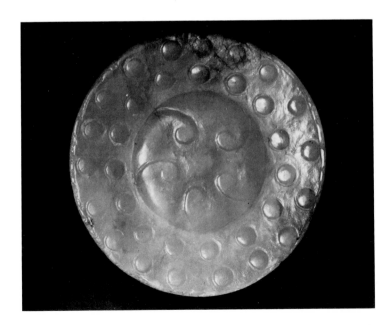

102.
Sword Pommel
Pale green nephrite with black flecks
Diam. 1 10/16"
Late Eastern Chou or Western Han

Raised central section has incised comma
pattern, the outer rim a series of circles
in relief. Allover soft polish. Reverse is flat,
with two conical horizontal perforations
in center, surrounded by deeply incised circle.
This was originally fashioned to fit the
top of a sword hilt, the circular groove on
the reverse permitting insertion. The
two additional perforations may have been
drilled later to facilitate use as a button.
Hansford illustrates a similar piece with the
same treatment on the reverse (No. 5B,
P. 98, No. C13).

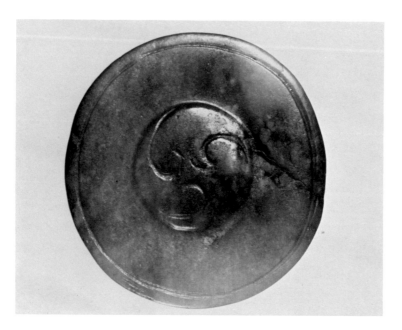

103.

Sword Pommel
Grey and brown nephrite
Diam. 1 6/16″
Late Eastern Chou or Western Han

Raised center section with incised comma
motif; incised circle near edge. Reverse
has two roughly cut perforations, and a
deep groove surrounding them. Soft allover
polish. Chêng writes that it was during
the Late Eastern Chou period that the practice
of making jade sword fittings began "a
system which was soon to be a standard
practice in the Han period." (**No. 3B**,
P. 197)

104.

Reshaped Pi
Dark green variegated nephrite
Diam. 10¾″
Late Eastern Chou or Western Han

Probably recut from original round shape.
Uneven conical perforation; shows drill
marks where cutting missed. Soft uneven
polish.

105.

Ts'ung
Medium to dark green altered nephrite
H. 3⅛"
Late Eastern Chou or Western Han

Short tube with square exterior. Softly sloping shoulders. Hole bored through evenly. Mellow polish (interior and exterior). The question as to whether this smaller type represented earth to the ancient Chinese has not been resolved. Willetts suggests that it might have been used as a wheel nave: "It is surely at least possible that they descend from a wooden Neolithic prototype which was a bearing inserted into the hub of the wheel, and inside which the axle rotated. That would account satisfactorily for their square outer perimeter...." (No. 14, P. 105)

Comparable example: No. 9B, Pp. 276-279.

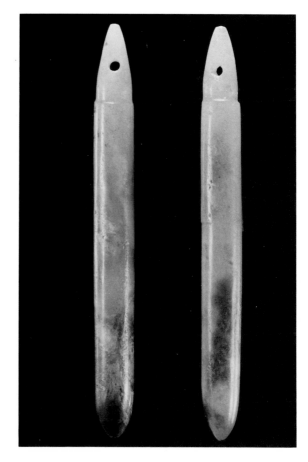

106.

Pair of Pendants
Pale green and rust-yellow nephrite
L. 2½"
Han?

Undecorated spikes with slight indentations at top, and perforations. Laufer suggests that they were worn as earrings or lady's hat decorations (No. 8, P. 254, Fig. 160), but their use has not been substantiated.

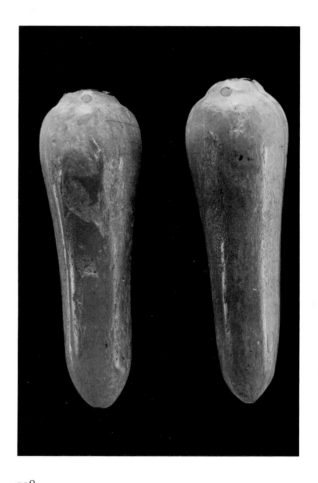

107.
Pendant
Pale green and buff altered nephrite,
incrustation of soil
L. 3″
Han?

Similar to preceding.

108.
Pair of Body Plugs?
Pale green altered nephrite
L. 1⅜″
Han?

Tapered, with soft allover polish. Tiny
perforation through top. It was the practice
to stop the orifices of the body with jade
plugs, in an effort to preserve the corpse. A
number of pieces for this purpose were
shown with the jade shroud of Prince Liu
Sheng in Peking (see cover of *Art News,*
March, 1972, lower right corner).

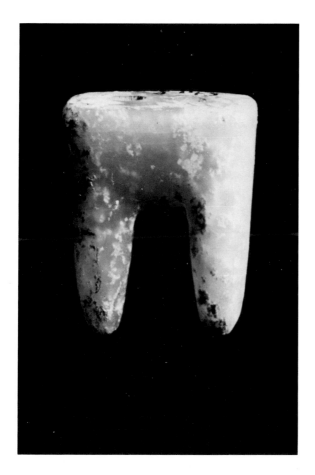

109.

Nose Plug?
Pale green and buff altered nephrite,
incrustation of soil
H. 1 4/16"
Han?

Double plug with allover soft polish. Flat top
having two conical horizontal perforations.

110.

Cicada (Tongue Amulet)
Olive green and white altered nephrite
L. 2"
Han Dynasty

Crudely worked stone, much decomposed
from burial, the features of the insect deeply
incised, eyes bulging at either side of head.
Incised on reverse with appropriate representation of the back of the insect. This type
of amulet was placed on the tongue of the
deceased at the time of burial. For an
explanation of the symbolism of the cicada
see catalogue No. 26.

Comparable example: **No. 9B, P. 393.**

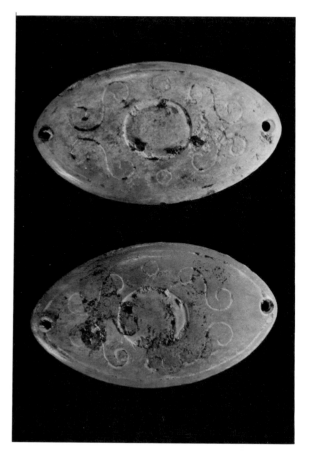

III.
Bead
Grey-green and buff altered nephrite
L. 1¼″
Han or earlier

Undecorated. Conical perforation through
center. Soft allover polish. Small chip.
Possibly from a necklace.

112.
Pair of Eye Covers
Grey-white altered nephrite, incrustation
of soil
L. 2″
Han

Oval placques incised with curvilinear motif.
Some soft polish remains. A conical
perforation at each end. Reverse undecorated,
slightly concave in center. Placques like
these were sometimes sewn to a veil or shroud
which covered the face of the dead (**No. 5A,**
Plate 27). Hansford also mentions that
these covers were placed on the eyes of the
deceased "to prevent the entry of evil or
destructive influences. . . ." (**No. 5B,** P. 99,
No. C15)

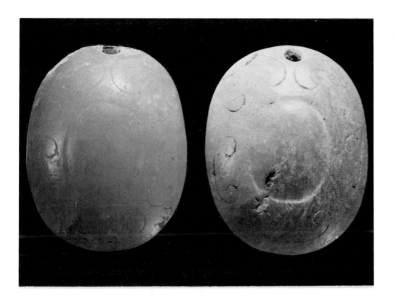

113.

Pair of Domed Placques
Grey-white nephrite, incrustation of soil
L. 1½"
Han

Incised with double curls, the reverse
undecorated and concave. Conical perforation
at top. Some soft polish remains. This
double curl motif can be seen on textiles of
the period (*The Silk Road,* Peking, 1973,
Plates 7, 8).

114.

Kuei-Pi
Grey, brown and rust altered nephrite
H. 4⅛"
Han or later

Pi (symbol of heaven) and *Kuei* (symbol of
rank) carved in one piece, the blade beveled
and tapering to a point at each end. Similar on
reverse. Perforation evenly drilled and
round. Hansford writes, "The ritual text
Chou li (third century B.C.) states that a
kuei-pi (or perhaps a *kuei* and a *pi*)
was used to sacrifice to the sun, moon and
stars...." (**No. 5B**, P. 178, No. E2)

Comparable example: **No. 8**, Plate XV,
No. 4.

115.
Kuei-Pi
Grey-white and brown altered nephrite,
incrustation of soil
L. 2 14/16″
Han

Incised curvilinear motif on *pi,* a blade
projecting at one end. The reverse flat and
undecorated. Perforation conical through
center. Some soft polish remains. Possibly
suspended from the girdle.

116.
Shield-Form Placque
Dark green altered nephrite
L. 4½″
Han

Slightly convex with curled motif incised on
front, a loop at each upper corner, the reverse
undecorated and concave. Use unknown.
The inverted heart-shaped form (top center
of decoration) seen here and on the next
example, appears on fabrics of the period
("Relics from a Han Tomb," *China
Reconstructs,* September, 1972, P. 25, upper
left corner).

117.
Shield-Form Placque
Grey and white altered nephrite, incrustation
of soil
L. 3¾"
Han

Tapering form with incised curvilinear
motifs, the reverse concave and undecorated.
A loop at either side, and perforation
through top. Use unknown.

118.
Bangle
Grey-green, black and brown nephrite,
incrustation of soil, red pigment
Diam. 3 1/16"
Han

Heavy bracelet, irregularly formed, the
exterior having an alternating design of
incised lines and double curl motifs in
low relief. One area has thick red pigment
with textile impression. The piece may have
been leaning against silk fabric in the
tomb, or originally wrapped in silk for burial.
Chêng writes that a metal wire in tension
(saw) was used from Chou times on
(**No. 3B**, P. 185) which produced fine
incised lines like those seen on this example.
The double curl motif is quite typical of
Han decoration as we have seen. These two
characteristics help to date this bracelet, and
the practice of wearing jade jewelry
continues in our time.

Bibliography

1. Andersson, J. G., *Bulletin Museum of Far Eastern Antiquities,* No. 15, 1943.

2. d'Argencé, R., *Chinese Jades in The Avery Brundage Collection,* 1972.

3. Chêng, Tê-k'un, Archaeology in China, Vol. I, *Prehistoric China,* 1966 (reprint).

3A. —— Archaeology in China, Vol. II, *Shang China,* 1960.

3B. —— Archaeology in China, Vol. III, *Chou China,* 1963.

4. Dohrenwend, D., *Chinese Jades in The Royal Ontario Museum,* 1971.

5. Hansford, S. H., *Chinese Jade Carving,* 1950.

5A. —— *Chinese Carved Jades,* 1968.

5B. —— *Jade-Essence of Hills and Streams,* 1969.

6. K'ao-ku.

7. K'ao-ku Hsüeh-pao.

8. Laufer, B., *Jade,* 1912.

9. Loehr, M., *Early Chinese Jades,* University of Michigan, 1953.

9A. —— *Relics of Ancient China,* The Asia Society, Inc., 1965.

9B. —— *Ancient Chinese Jades,* Fogg Art Museum, 1975.

10. Salmony, A., *Carved Jade of Ancient China,* 1938.

10A. —— "Collecting Ancient Chinese Jades: A Popular Hobby in China and Here," Buffalo Museum of Science, Fascicle No. 2, (reprinted from *Hobbies,* Dec., 1944, Vol. 25, No. 2).

10B. —— *Archaic Chinese Jades,* (Sonnenschein Collection), 1952.

10C. —— *Chinese Jade Through The Wei Dynasty,* 1963.

11. "3000 Years of Chinese Jade," Arden Gallery, 1939.

12. Watson, Wm., *Archaeology in China,* 1960.

12A. —— *Cultural Frontiers in Ancient East Asia,* 1971.

13. Wen Wu.

14. Willetts, Wm., *Chinese Art,* I, 1958 (Penguin paperback).